THINK OUTSIDE THE BOX

SUTEKI CREATIVE

Justine Avery & Liuba Syrotiuk

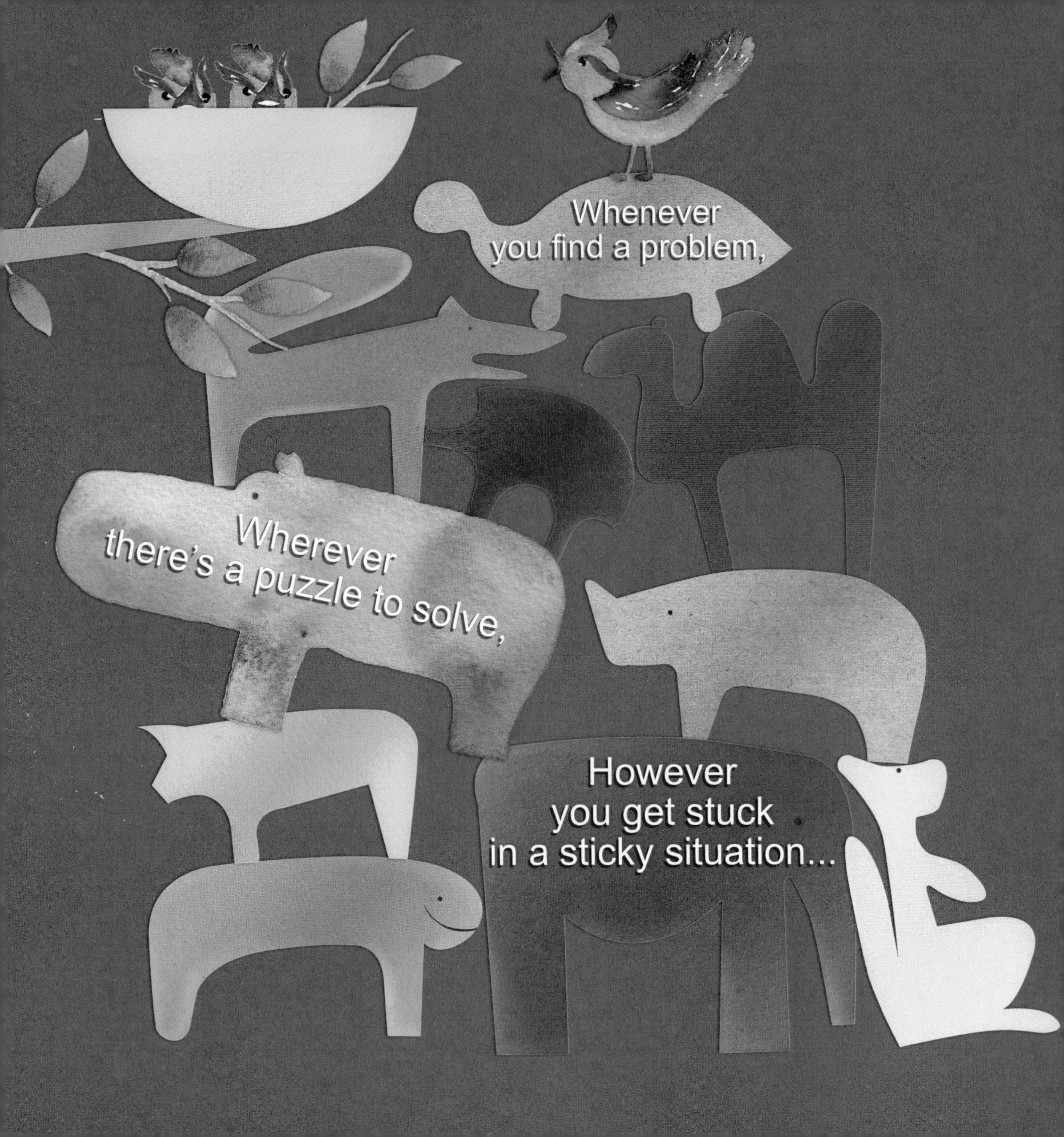
Whenever you find a problem,
Wherever there's a puzzle to solve,
However you get stuck in a sticky situation...

Just *think outside the box.*

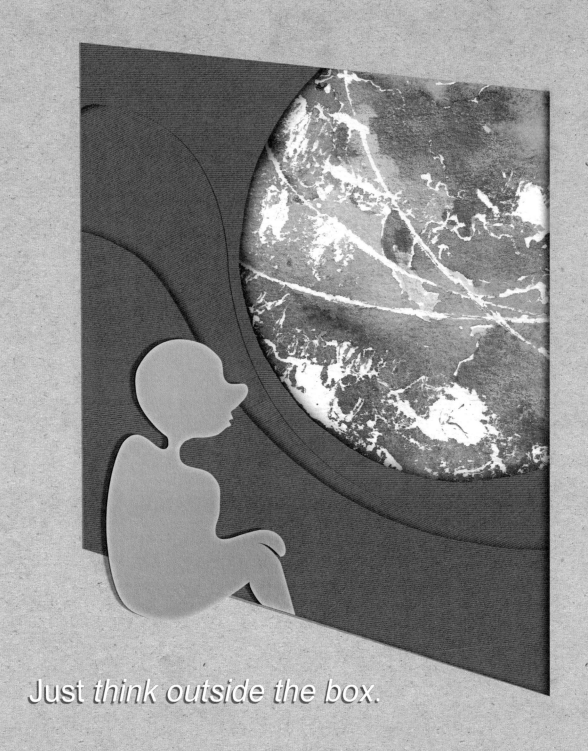

Just *think outside the box.*

OUTSIDE
THE BOX

And seeing through
your own personal view.

But *think* what your super brain might think...

If you could place it *outside* your own head!

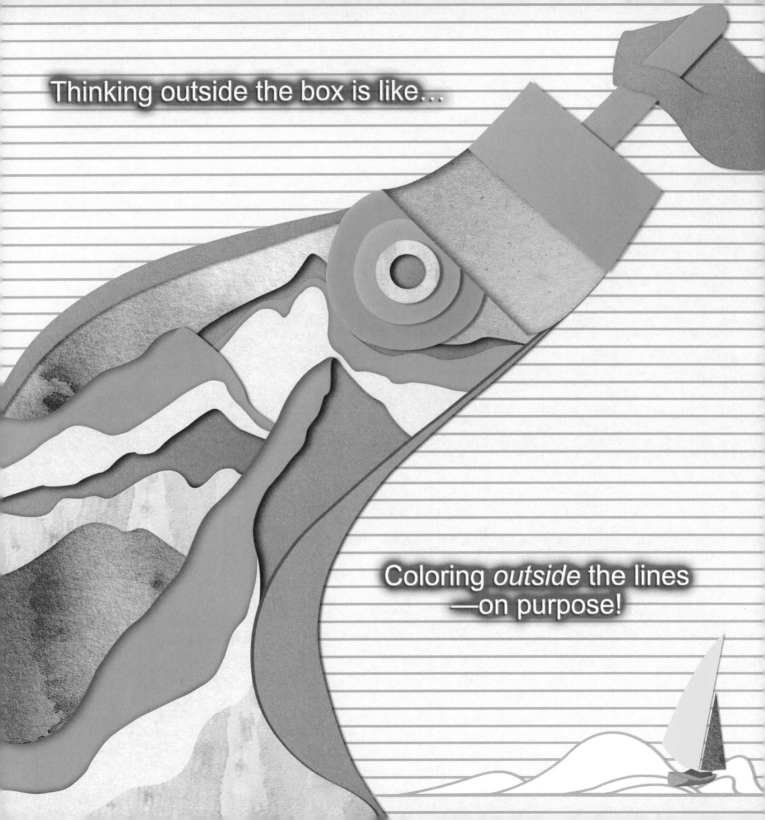

Thinking outside the box is like...

Coloring *outside* the lines —on purpose!

Or doing the *opposite* of the most obvious thing.

It's like trying to run a race
the *slowest.*

Or eating
an ice cream cone

from the bottom up.

It's like checking out the view...

While standing *super tall*
on something *way up high*.

It's like looking at a problem...

While you're *upside down.*

Or standing in *someone else's* shoes.

And wait for the new ideas
to *come to you*.

Thinking outside the box means to be *creative*.

It's noticing the details that
no one else sees.

It's the same as *slowing down*
—or even stopping—
when everyone else is rushing around.

Or taking the time to *listen* instead of talking.

It's always being
proud of your mistakes.

Because they're just as valuable
as every time
you *get things right*.

You will never stay stuck,

Or run out of luck,

If you remember
to think *outside* the box.

To everyone, everywhere...
Remember that creativity is everything.
Let yours guide you.
—J.A.

This book is dedicated to my grandmother Nadine whose originative, positive thinking changes many lives and inspires creativity.
—L.S.

Justine Avery is an award-winning author who loves writing stories for all sorts of readers. She was born in America but grew up-and is still growing up-all over the world as a natural explorer with a curiosity for all things. She's jumped out of airplanes, off of very high bridges, and into shark-infested waters-to name a few adventures. And books are her favorite adventures of all.

Liuba Syrotiuk is a Ukrainian designer and watercolor artist. She works as an interior designer and watercolor illustrator. Liuba is a bright and sunny person, willing to find beauty in everything, especially in nature. Traveling around the world with a small box of watercolors makes her the happiest person.

FIRST EDITION

Copyright © 2020 Justine Avery
Illustrated by Liuba Syrotiuk
All rights reserved.

First published 2020
by Suteki Creative

ISBN: 978-1-948124-56-0
ISBN: 978-1-948124-58-4 (hardcover)
ISBN: 978-1-948124-55-3 (ebook)

But *please do...*
lend this book freely!
It's *yours*—you own it. So, pass it on, trade it in, exchange it with and recommend it to other readers. Books are the very best gifts.

Discover More...
uniquely wonderful, utterly imaginative children's books by Justine Avery

978-1-948124-37-9

978-1-948124-29-4

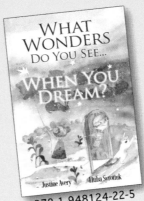

978-1-948124-22-5

978-1-948124-45-4

978-1-948124-41-6

978-1-948124-53-9

978-1-948124-49-2

Visit JustineAvery.com and join in the exclusive fun & freebies.

Made in the USA
Coppell, TX
01 November 2020